C000213558

GORDON WILYMAN
Memoirs of a
Welsh Halfbred

Gordon Wilyman
Memoirs of a Welsh Halfbred

Gordon Wilyman and Meurig Owen

Foreword by David Walters
Chief Executive of the Royal Welsh Show

Part of the proceeds from the sale
of this book will be donated to the
Royal Agricultural Benevolent Institution (RABI)

© Text: Gordon Wilyman/Meurig Owen

All rights reserved.
No part of this publication may be reproduced,
stored in a retrieval system, or transmitted in any form or by
any means, electronic, electrostatic, magnetic tape, mechanical,
photocopying, recording, or otherwise, without prior
permission of the authors of the works herein.

ISBN: 0-86381-901-X

Cover design: Sian Parri

First published in 2004 by the author;
printed by Gwasg Carreg Gwalch, Llanrwst.

To Winnie and John

Contents

Acknowledgements

Our warmest thanks to several people for their help: Captain Nick Archdale; Meuric Rees; Idwal Vaughan, Llangernyw; Bob Hughes, Llanfair Talhaearn; Roger Wilyman; John Hooson; Elfed Williams; Angus Chalmers, Secretary of the Oxford Farming Conference; Gill Napper, General Secretary of the Welsh Halfbred Sheep Breeders Association; Professor Hywel Wyn Owen, University of Wales Bangor and Menna Owen who did the typing and gave valuable editorial advice.

Our particular thanks are due to David Walters, Chief Executive of the Royal Welsh Agricultural Society for writing the foreword.

Gordon Wilyman and Meurig Owen

Foreword by David Walters, BSc(Hons), FRAgS, Chief Executive Royal Welsh Agricultural Society

Gordon Wilyman is unique. He was brought up and educated in Birmingham. Despite this suburban background, however, and against active family disapproval, he set his mind on a farming career. Remarkably he survived all the hazards; the hard work, the lack of cash to get a foothold on the farming ladder and the family dissent, merely strengthened his resolve. Gordon Wilyman was to become one of the country's leading exponents of successful sheep farming and hill management and notably a founder member of the team who established the hybrid Welsh Halfbred ewe which was to revolutionise the outlook for hill farmers.

Here you will read of his progress through the ranks as a working pupil on farms in Warwick and Cheshire culminating in his first toe-hold on the farming ladder, a 17 acre pig farm at Ewloe in north east Wales. Progressing from there to a share farming opportunity on a 630 acre hill farm, with 'cynefin' on the Denbigh Moors, which almost went wrong. But Gordon isn't one to walk away from a challenge: here you will read how he transformed Melai into an upland farm showcase.

His valuable work on NFU committees (he has been an NFU man for over 60 years); Pwllpeirian; National Ministry Advisory Committees; and as a Meat and Livestock Commissioner for Wales is faithfully recorded. His address to the Oxford Farming Conference in 1973 is included as is his part in founding the Welsh Halfbred Sheep Breeders Association with which he will always be identified.

He has been a frequent judge and exhibitor at the Royal Welsh Show and it is for this reason, if for no other, that I have pleasure in writing the foreword and commending this book. It has given me the opportunity to salute Gordon's outstanding service to the farming community and country life.

Prelude

Gordon Wilyman OBE, FRAgS was born on March 2, 1915 in Warwickshire. His father was of Lincolnshire stock, his mother a Warwickshire lady – neither of a truly rural inclination. His upbringing and education was in Birmingham. Both his brothers Ken, three years older and Peter, five years his junior, pursued careers totally different from that of Gordon, who went on to become one of the most highly respected authorities on sheep breeding and hill farming of his generation. His advice sought on numerous farming committees was based on sound practical experience, much of it gained the hard way. In 1954 he was appointed on to the Pwllpeirian Hill Farming Advisory Committee on which he served for fifteen years; in 1962 appointed on to the Minister's Hill Farming Committee for Wales which he chaired for seven years; in 1966 appointed to the Ministry's Hill Farming Advisory Committee for England, Wales and Northern Ireland of which he was deputy chairman for eight years. In 1973 he was appointed a Welsh Commissioner on the Meat and Livestock Commission – chairing its Sheep Advisory Committee for eight years, and in 1978 addressing the Oxford Farming Conference. But his name as a farming visionary and leader was already established, when in 1953 with eleven others, he founded the hybrid Welsh Halfbred, a cross, mating the Welsh Mountain Ewe with a Border Leicester Ram, and arranging their marketing to buyers throughout the United Kingdom. This was to revolutionise the outlook for both the hill and lowland sheep farmer. His progress up the farming ladder culminating in Melai, a six hundred and thirty acre neglected hill farm with outlying cynefin for 350 ewes which he transformed into a farming showcase visited, admired and often copied, had been far from easy. There were times when lesser mortals would have packed it all in, but in all this Gordon had a constant ally in his wife

Winnie. For over sixty years she had been his power base and inspiration – from the early days of their married life at a seventeen acre pig farm in a one up – one down cottage at Ewloe in Flintshire, later progressing to half a larger house (where both their sons where born) to the greatest challenge of his farming life at Melai, a hill farm six miles up country from Abergele. Often strapped for cash, Gordon knows full well the anxiety of second mortgages and big overdrafts, but still his resolve held good. Such were the risks, but there was also the blind faith in his own ability. His is a story of struggle by a farming visionary prepared to try out new farming concepts, often at high stakes – and winning.

It's a story with a lot of humour, looking at life in retrospect is often like that, but at the last there is a cruel twist of fate: his eldest son John in his early fifties contracted motor – neurone disease while Winnie was afflicted by the dreaded Alzheimer's – both died within a year of each other. Melai was sold in July 2002. This, in his own words, is Gordon Wilyman's life story . . .

Part I

Chapter 1

Rotten Jobs at Uncle Charlie's

I was born at Wellesbourne a Warwickshire village midway between Warwick and Stratford upon Avon where my father was a private estate agent for an American millionaire – millionaires were a very rare specie at the beginning of the century – on an estate called Morton Morrell. Wellesbourne was on the edge of the Morton Morrell estate. My father was also in the Warwickshire Yeomanry and as soon as the 1914 war started he was called up and was posted to France and was there for the whole of the war serving in the Battle of the Somme, leaving the army with the rank of captain. Meantime his duties on the estate were taken over by his elder brother Arthur who had suffered from polio as a child and was declared unfit for national service. After the war when my father came out of the army, Emmet, the American millionaire owner of the estate, had been killed in the war. His wife then decided to sell the estate and go back to America. Of course, my father's position was precarious, not only had we lost the house which was on the estate but it meant that he had also lost his job. He then began something completely new to him, starting with the firm of W. & T. Avery the weighing machine people as a clerk, he went on to become their financial adviser! So we then moved from Wellesbourne to a place called Handsworth near Birmingham. I suppose it would be about 1920 and I would then be about 5 or 6 years old. After attending Grove Lane Council School there, I went to Aston Grammar on the outskirts of Birmingham and moved on from there to King Edward's, a Public Day School in the middle of the city right by New Street Station (which was bombed in the last war) and left that school in 1932. This incidentally was also where my elder brother Ken attended with Enoch Powell as a class mate, which developed into a lifelong friendship.

During our time living in the Birmingham area, friends of my parents used to call in, and although little boys and children generally at that time were seen and not heard, occasionally one would say to me: 'What do you want to do Gordon when you leave school?' And where a lot of children would say I want to be a train driver or a fireman, I always said right from the very early days: 'I want to be a farmer'. And they looked at me as if I was a little bit touched. The reason why I said that I wanted to be a farmer was because my Uncle Charlie had a farm at a place called Budbrooke – Church Farm – which was three miles out of Warwick. He had married my mother's eldest sister, and in the school holidays I used to go to stay with them and that was the highlight of the year. That was where I learnt and saw what went on in farming, and made up my mind straight away that this was what I wanted to do. In 1932 when I was 17 I left school and I still said I wanted to be a farmer. My father, of course, had just come through the General Strike of 1926, and in the early thirties industry and everything was in the depths of depression: more people were going out of farming than were trying to get into it. My father said to me: 'Wouldn't you rather be an estate agent or anything?'. But I was adamant that I wanted to be a farmer, and so to try and break me of this crazy notion he said, 'you had better go and spend six or twelve months with your Uncle Charlie'. Unknown to me, he had told my uncle to set me on the worst possible jobs on the farm to break me of this stupid idea. So I went to Uncle Charlie's which was quite a large mainly, arable farm, and was with him for nearly twelve months. There were generally three teams of horses ploughing in one field, and there I, a callow town youth, learnt how to handle a team of cart horses. I had to plough a single ten inch furrow through heavy

Warwickshire clay with two horses: the head carter was in front while I was in the middle, and the other carter at the back of me, which meant that I had to keep up with the leader. And for the first three days it nearly killed me, because, if you've ever ploughed with horses, you'll know that when you get to the headland to turn and come back again the horses do all the work. You merely tilt the plough to the side and let the horses take it round, but of course I didn't realise how to do this and I was trying to manhandle it round to start with, so that for the first two days I thought I would finish with farming for ever!

But I didn't and I still enjoyed what I did. You must remember in those days farming was completely different to what it is today. People say to me now through these bad years we've just had with farming, 'you must remember the thirties, we're getting back to that', and my reply to that is, 'we are not, because in the depression that agriculture has just been through, all the inputs have gone up in price and our outputs have been worth less. In the thirties everything was cheap: everything the farmer bought was cheap, and the produce he sold was cheap, that is the difference.'

As I mentioned earlier there wasn't a tractor anywhere, it was all horse work so everything had to be pulled, pushed, shoveled or lifted, it was all manual work.

Church Farm was a grain growing farm, and the grain used to go away on the railway from Warwick station, the wheat in sacks weighing two and a quarter hundredweights.

Two men lifted these on to horse drawn wagons to go to the station, using a wooden bar which was held, one in the left hand one in the right, a man on either side, using the free hand to heave the sack over.

It was not an easy life: there was no electricity, there was no mains water – all the water had to be pumped into a tank with a hand pump every night to get some water into the taps in the house. And after a hard day's work my aunt used to say to me: 'Well you'd better pump the water into the house now', and it would take me at least half an hour of hard work to pump the water out of the well into the tank. And things were so bad, that at meal times the pudding was always served before the meat, the idea being that if you filled yourself up with a lot of spotted dick and treacle puddings, you wouldn't eat so much meat, which was more expensive. This was the general custom on farms throughout Warwickshire. And then of course, there were only outside double seater loos, and it was my job to empty them because unbeknown to me I was doing the worst jobs my uncle could find!

Several things come to mind. My uncle ran a flock of about two hundred ewes on the farm and when it came time in the Spring for the lambs to be castrated he had his own system of doing the job. Uncle Charlie was quite a heavily built man with a large moustache, and the custom was that the farm men would lift the lambs on to their shoulders, holding the legs suitably separated while he cut the testicle bag with a sharp knife and drew them out with his teeth. After he had done six or so, the blood would be streaming down his moustache. He wasn't normally a heavy drinking man but he certainly drank a lot of beer at castrating time, and at the end of the day's work, feasting on a supper of fried lamb's testicles known as lamb's fries at the kitchen table. It wasn't a meal that I particularly relished after seeing the performance in the lamb pens! Such were my early days in farming, but my resolve was as strong as ever. After spending twelve months with my uncle, father realized I was going to be a farmer no matter what!

It is of interest to note that J.R.R. Tolkien (1892-1972) the South African-born philologist and author who wrote 'The Lord of the Rings' trilogy was educated at King Edward VI School. As Gordon observes it was bombed in the war, and the site has been developed into a shopping parade.

Chapter 2

The Rocky Road to Melai

At that time more people were trying to get out of farming than were getting into it. My father asked me, 'what sort of farming do you want to do?' As it was a mixed farm that my uncle had, with a herd of about twenty cows which were hand milked, I said that I would like to go into dairying. My father knew a little about agriculture having been an estate agent, so he said that the prime dairy farming county was Cheshire, and we had better go and see what was available there. I'm not quite sure who his contact was, but we went into Cheshire to a farm on the Wirral called Collinge Farm at Backford, which was farmed by a man called Edward Carter.

And after going there and talking to him, Mr Carter agreed to take me on as a working pupil. And working was the operative word! We started at six in the morning and finished at six at night six days a week, with Sunday, depending on the time of the year, being a bit easier of course. As with most Cheshire farms they milked about a hundred cows, and as there weren't any machines at that time they were all hand milked.

The wives of the men who worked on the farm all had to turn up, it was part of the agreement of taking on a man, that his wife also milked. And most of the women seemed to have a baby every year, so that they'd turn up with two babies in the pram and another one running around at milking time. Each was supposed to milk twelve cows by hand and it was quite a job carrying all the milk with two pails on a yolk to the dairy to be cooled.

We agreed with Edward Carter that he would take me on and that I would live with the family in the house, learning the ropes as a working pupil. They were an extremely nice family. I thought that he was a hard man but he wasn't hard, it was the times that were hard. I got to like him very much and the food was good. Mrs Carter had the groceries and household needs delivered to the farm every week, which regularly included her husband's smoking requirements. That amounted to 7 packs of 20 Capstan full strength cigarettes, 7 ounces of Airman Flake tobacco and 7 boxes of matches. Every morning Mr Carter, then in his sixties, would put a packet of cigarettes and an ounce of tobacco in his pocket together with a box of matches – and he got through them all every day of his life. And he lived on well into his eighties!

I was paid ten shillings every other week, and it was the custom for the boss to pay the wages during milking time on a Friday night when the milk women and the men were all there. On the weeks that I was to get mine he would give me a ten shilling note and look at me almost as though I was overpaid, and the next week when I got nothing he just walked straight past and ignored me. But I did like the man, he was a very pleasant chap and after the first winter on the farm when the spring came he said to me: 'Gordon would you like the chance to earn some overtime?' I said 'yes of course I would', so he said, 'would you like to take on the muck spreading?' All the manure was carried out with a horse and cart and there were seven heaps of manure to each cart load, which was hooked out on to the field at regular intervals.

And so my job in the spring was to go muck spreading. This was after a hard day's work, so after I'd had my supper at night I'd go out with a fork to spread this manure. After the first fortnight I finished up with a lot of blisters and not very much money! Later I got into the hang of it, it had to be spread very finely because this was an all grass farm, and if it wasn't spread finely the boss would look at it on a Friday night before I had my 'overtime pay', and say you'd better go back to that field and go over it again. For this I was paid a half penny a heap, and after a fortnight when I got into the hang of it, I found I could do sixteen heaps an hour. That came to eight pence which was the overtime rate for a farm man, so I thought I was doing well there; it was in addition to my ten shillings every other week, and in addition to that, my father used to send me a pound every month just to help things out. The pound plus the ten shillings every other week was supposed to suffice my night needs for wine women and song, so you can imagine I didn't do very much singing. But it was surprising how rich I felt after spreading this manure at the rate of sixteen heaps an hour! It must be remembered that everything was so much cheaper then. I stayed with Edward Carter at Collinge Farm for about eighteen months, and then my father said: 'You know there are other things than work on a farm, so I think you'd better go to agricultural college for a course'. In 1934 I went to Reese Heath College near Nantwich, where the head was W.B Mercer, to take a mixed agricultural course, staying there for eight months. It was a coeducational college with the women students taking dairy courses, but there was absolutely no fraternizing allowed. We were in separate hostels, and to talk to a girl out of the hostel was a thing to incur the wrath of the head, you didn't get away with that. Except on a Saturday night when there was a dance in the girls hostel. There we boys were under the strict eye of the matron, if we danced more than twice with the same girl she would come over and have something to say about it!

When I left Rease Heath I went on to another farm three miles out of Chester, at Huntington called Huntington Old Hall, which was farmed by John Bate. This was a cheese making farm, again still hand milking. There were 120 cows and all the milk was made into cheese. The head cheese maker ruled the farm, certainly at mid day, because as soon as the milk in the vat was ready to be cut, it had to be formed into a curd and drained ready to be stacked in presses. If you were in the middle of your lunch it didn't matter one bit, if the cheese maker said it was ready, everyone had to drop their tools, knives and forks and go to help. I learnt a lot about cheese making there.

Chester Young Farmers Cub at this time proved to be an important part of my life, becoming its chairman in 1937. This interest had begun whilst I was at Edward Carter's where his son Geoffrey, eight years older than myself had taken me along to their monthly meetings, lectures and so on. It was an all lads club in those days. And while I was there going to these meetings with Geoffrey Carter, there were two brothers who also went, they were called Charlie and Sam Pym and through them I met their sister Winifred. And of course we were married later. She was the cheese maker on their family farm.

After I'd been at Huntingdon Old Hall with John Bate for probably twelve months, I heard of someone who wanted an assistant on a farm called Golbourne Hall at Handley which was near Tattenhall about eight miles from Chester. So I applied for the job and I got it, and became assistant to a Mr Huxley who was the boss. I was in charge of the men when he was away. But although there were milking machines at Golbourne Hall there were still no tractors. I worked as assistant manager there for about two years on thirty shillings a week and my keep. It was considered to be quite a reasonable wage, but naturally I was unable to save a lot of money. After I'd been with Harry Huxley for nearly two years, my previous employer John Bate from Huntingdon came to me one day and said, 'I hear there's a small farm with a big piggery that's going to be let, at a place called Ewloe in Flintshire.' He said it would be an ideal way to get into farming with very little capital. This was good because I'd been unable to save very much, it was a way to enable me to get a foot on the farming ladder. John Bate said 'I'll come with you and look at this place', which was called Ewloe Hall; it was nothing like a hall and there was certainly no big house. It had at one time been a stud farm for a man called Kenyon, who was one of the top breeders of hackney horses in the country. He had put up a lot of indoor stabling and riding school and then decided to move out. It was then bought by Johnny Williams who converted the riding school and boxes into piggeries, creating housing for about 250 pigs. This was the property that was to be let, together with seventeen acres of very poor land. The rent was fifty pounds a year with an option on a very small one-up-one-down cottage adjoining, for a further ten pounds. John Bate advised that I should go for it. This was in 1938 and I was unmarried. So I realised that here was my opportunity to get on to the farming ladder. I reasoned if you had a wheelbarrow and a shovel and some buckets, you did not need much more, and so I took this farm and went there to live in this little one-up-one-down cottage. I had savings of £190 pounds at that time and my father said he would lend £500 to help me, on which I had to pay interest. John Bate (the Cheshire Cheese man) who had come with me said, 'I will put an insurance policy, as security, at the bank so that you can have an overdraft of £150'. That was my entire working capital to start farming.

This was to be a pig fattening unit: feed had to be bought in and I would need to attend local markets to buy weaner pigs. But I certainly couldn't afford to buy a car so, I bought a motor bike to go around places like Holywell, Wrexham and Mold to buy store pigs, and I also took jobbing work on a neighbouring farm for Ted Williams on a part time basis. When he wanted some extra labour, I would go and work there: things went well. I calculated that by looking after things properly: buying eight week old weaner pigs as small as I could get them, and selling them off as baconers left a margin of £1 a pig, which was quite a lot of money. After about four months (this was in 1938) I was doing well and putting some money together, then the war started and feeding stuff went into short supply. All livestock were put on rations based on the previous two years purchases. But because I had only started my farming less than two years previously, my purchases were not very large, so my rations allocation was small. But I managed to eke out the rations with some stuff which was called Tottenham Pudding.

It was called Tottenham Pudding because it originated in Tottenham where the Council bought all the kitchen waste from houses and hotels and boiled it, then got the water out and sold it as a pudding. A firm in Liverpool started producing it and I got in with them: each of these puddings was delivered in half barrels weighing about a hundredweight and a half and emptied at the farm in a fairly solid mass. So for a few months, to help out with the rations, my pigs were fed Tottenham Pudding, which was a great help. It was broken up and tipped into the pig troughs topped with some barley meal. The pigs did well on it and it kept me going. Surprisingly the puddings contained all manner of kitchen cutlery which the pigs simply left behind, not affected one bit: I could have easily lain several kitchen tables with what the pigs left in the troughs after feeding time! And I still worked for this other farmer. After a time I was able to take on Crosstree Farm, Buckley, a small sixty acre adjoining farm on let, in addition to the pig farm. The work had now become too much for one person so I had to employ a man to help me. I was still ploughing with a team of horses, and of course during the war everyone had to plough a certain percentage of their land to produce corn and potatoes.

Winnie and I were now married, we tied the knot in 1939, but I wasn't at all popular with my in-laws. They had expected their daughter to do a lot better than marry a struggling pig farmer. And the prospect of her living in the rather grandly called Ewloe Hall one-up-one-down cottage didn't endear me to them. Although we were able, a little later, to move into part of a bigger house. It was a marriage that lasted over sixty very happy years, we were soul mates; without her I couldn't have achieved very much. Decisions were discussed and shared; a helping hand on the farm, Winnie was ever ready to do that too. She was an excellent home maker, needle woman, flower arranger and gardener – and a first rate cook. It was a joke in our family that I'd married her for her eccles cakes! Although she was a Cheshire farmer's daughter there was certainly no marriage dowry, after all she had two brothers both intent on going into farming.

I joined the NFU in June 1938 soon after I went to the pig farm, so looking back, my connection with the farmers union up to when I retired in 2002 is well over sixty years! Most of the Farmers Union group secretaries in those days were part time people, many were farmers themselves and they did the secretarial work for very little money at night. I joined the NFU, because whilst at the Chester YFC, I had met a young man called Ritchie Ross who later became a Group Secretary: he came to see me, and at his bidding, I joined the NFU Hawarden branch. Hawarden was very close to where I lived so I naturally went to their branch meetings. It wasn't long before I became a delegate to the Flintshire Executive which had its monthly meetings in Mold. After I had been on the executive a while I was made chairman of their Livestock and Wool Committee. And it was while I was attending these meetings in Mold that I got quite friendly with a man called Edward Owen who farmed Gwernigron near St Asaph. Edward Owen came to me one day, knowing that I was looking for a better and bigger farm. He had sold Gwernigron, a four hundred acre farm of prime land for, I think, £56,000, which was an absolutely unheard of figure in those days: it made sensational news throughout Wales. Having sold the farm, he then saw a hill farm advertised called Melai and bought it. I think it caught him on the back foot really, because as soon as he had bought it he realised that it was a young man's farm: it was a hill farm and it wasn't really for him. He didn't want to go to live there, and it was when I was talking to him one night at the Flintshire Executive that he asked me would I consider renting a hill farm. I said, 'I know nothing at all about hill farming but I am interested,' and so he said, 'would you like to come and see it?'. I said 'Oh very much'. So I went with Edward Owen one day up to this farm Melai, which was in fairly rough condition. It had been farmed by a cattle dealer called Shadrach Davies who was probably

26

more interested in his dealing. It was more a place for his dealing activities and he had held annual sales there: this was the farm Edward Owen had bought. And we went to look around this farm and he said, 'what do you think?' He told me what the rent would be and I said: 'Frankly it's the type of farming I know nothing at all about, but I'm certainly interested'. And so he said, 'well do you want another look round'. So I met him again on another day. And the next time I met him he said, 'I'm so sorry but I can't let the farm'. I realised afterwards why: one of his daughters was going out with Edgar Rees a Denbigh solicitor, and I think Edgar had advised his prospective father in law. It was very good advice – there was no question about that, it would be a stupid thing to do, because once you had let a farm in those days you'd let it for life, and you couldn't get the tenant out. Whatever happened, Edward Owen was withdrawing his offer of a tenancy, but he had another proposition to make: 'Would you consider a partnership?'

Farming partnerships fifty years ago were almost unheard of. He knew I hadn't a lot of capital and he said, 'you can put whatever capital you can manage into the farm, I'll put the balance, you will manage it and run it and we will talk the policy over together', and I was to get a certain percentage for my managerial work there. I've forgotten what salary it was but I agreed on it. So we went into this working partnership and I must say it really worked very well. We never had a wrong word, but it was understood that after about three years when I felt that I had got enough money, I could pay him out and take it over on my own account. But it required a lot of money to stock 630 acres.

After three years Edward Owen came to me one day and said that he wanted to get out, 'You'll have to pay me out'. Both his daughters were getting married, Mair was marrying Edgar Rees, Morfudd was marrying John Tudor a Dolgellau veterinary surgeon, and I think that he wanted to give them a

27

helping hand, and that was the reason why Edward Owen wanted to get out.

I almost had to pack it up, it made things very difficult, but I went to the bank and took out second mortgages and that sort of thing and was able to do it, so in the end I paid Edward Owen out. I took the farm over on my own from 1953 and that's how I came to be at Melai. It was a completely new type of farming for me. Farming wasn't very highly mechanized even then, there were tractors of course, but still quite a lot of work was done by horses. It was all a very interesting challenge.

I took on the shepherd, Bob Hughes, who had been on the farm for six years before, so he was a wonderful help to me and three other men were taken on: that is how I started in Melai. I never ever had a wrong word with Edward Owen; we were good friends, and I visited him right up to the time that he died at over a hundred years of age at The Meadows Nursing Home near St Asaph.

Chapter 3

Sheep Farming – Learning the Ropes.

Melai was 630 acres on the 550 – 1100 foot contour with further unfenced grazing rights for 350 Welsh ewes six miles away up on the Hiraethog Mountain. It was my good fortune that Bob Hughes, the young shepherd who had been at Melai for six years before I came on the scene, agreed to stay on with me. He was an excellent sheep man and taught me all I know about the business. This had been his life since childhood.

Bob Hughes became a close and trusted friend, the relationship never a boss and employee one. I wouldn't have achieved anything without him and the other good men who worked with me.

With their help I soon learnt about 'y cynefin', the grazing custom on the mountain where sheep indigenous to their territory stay in their given area: sharing the mountain with my neighbours, Wynne Finch and the Crossleys on the far side. After a time, like everyone else, we realised that the draft ewes would be much more profitable if, after they had done four years on the mountain, they were crossed for lowland lamb production.

Melai was big enough to keep all the draft ewes from the mountain so we never sold them, and we then started crossing those older Welsh Mountain ewes with a Border Leicester ram. I don't know how it came about but Bob Hughes reckons that Edward Owen, during our three year partnership, had brought lambs of this cross to Melai for fattening and one way or another they must have demonstrated potential.

However I went to Mold market one day and met a butcher there called Bill Lewis and his brother Edwin, who also had a farm and were bringing in lots of Border Leicester rams to the auction. I bought some Border Leicesters off them and started crossing them with the Welsh draft ewes from the mountain. After about two years a number of us got together, and decided that mating the Welsh mountain ewe with a Border Leicester ram was a cross which was genetically compatible: the first cross had the vigour of the Welsh mountain ewe, but was bigger, and had the ability to forage and produce larger sized lambs.

We discovered that several of us were doing the same thing from this area, Nick Archdale was one, from Penbedw, near Mold. So after a very short time we decided to form an association with an annual sale where we would be selling nothing but Welsh Halfbred ewe lambs or ewes. The first one in this area was held in the Harp Yard Auction of Jones & Beardmore at Abergele, and such was the demand for the new hybrid that some farmers in the Builth Wells area started the same thing there. Soon we got together and decided to form the Welsh Halfbred Sheep Breeders Association. There are only three of the founder members left now, I am one, Nick Archdale from Penbedw is another, and the third is a man called Francis Morris who now lives in Leominster.

But having started these two sales, we then went from Abergele to Llangollen for our annual sale. This is how that came about: while at Abergele we had received great help from Henry Jones of Beardmore's who became our enthusiastic secretary, so when Henry left Beardmore's to join Jones and Son of Wrexham and St Asaph, the move to Llangollen market, and then to a good roadside site at Llanddyn Hall, Llangollen belonging to Jack Edwards, with different auctioneers made good sense.

We then decided to have a committee, because the first two sales were drawing sheep which were very questionable Halfbreds. When the original Halfbreds were again put to a Border Leicester tup, the resulting progeny was totally out of character and such specimens were turning up at our sales. We realised that we had to have some very strict rules, with inspectors to cull any sheep that, in their opinion, were not true to type. It wasn't a popular move, nothing like that had ever happened at sales before. We appointed inspectors from north Wales to inspect the sheep in south Wales, and inspectors from south Wales to inspect the sheep in north Wales, with strict authority to reject animals which did not meet our standards.

The buyers in the end got to know that the sheep that they were buying were, not only inspected for breed type, but they were also guaranteed to be free from foot rot and of the age at which they were catalogued. They were the sort of conditions which had never before been implemented in the sheep industry in England, Scotland or Wales, and they went well with buyers who found they could purchase with greater confidence. These are conditions which are now accepted and used by other sheep breed societies at their sales. It wasn't long before we had buyers from Scotland, and almost all over England, and that's how the Welsh Halfbred Sheep Breeders Association started. After another four years there were a number of farmers in the Welshpool area who had been buying sheep, and they wanted to form their own society, so we then had annual sales in Builth, Llangollen and Welshpool with inspectors from the other regions to inspect the sheep.

*   *   *

My involvement with the Meat and Livestock Commission (MLC) as Welsh Commissioner came quite a bit later of course.

I was appointed on to some of the committees through my NFU involvement. I left the Flintshire County Branch when I came to Melai, and joined the NFU in Denbighshire who had their meetings in Ruthin (becoming County Chairman and President during the years 1962-64). And it was there, as chairman of the Livestock Committee, that my connection with the NFU Headquarters in London began. It was from there that I was asked in 1954 to serve on the Ministry's Pwllpeirian Hill

Farm Advisory Committee. Pwllpeirian was a true hill farm with higher land than we had: their bottom land started at a thousand feet! This was an interesting time to be there. The government at that time wanted greater production from the uplands, and were promoting various schemes to achieve this. Grants were liberally offered for draining and reseeding them: roadways to access them were grant aided. Pwllpeirian near Aberystwyth was the Ministry's proofing ground: a prototype to illustrate to hill farmers what was possible and how it could be done. In my fifteen years service there, I was able to put into good effect many of the things I had seen there, on my own farm. Now of course Pwllpeirian are allowing the re-seeded land to revert to natural pasture for nature conservation.

It was from here that I was asked to serve, in 1962, on the Ministry's Hill Farming Committee for Wales which I chaired for seven years, and in 1966, on to the Central Committee for England, Wales and Northern Ireland. I then went to meetings in London about hill sheep farming matters, and after a few years was made vice chairman of that committee.

The chairman in essence was always a member of parliament, a cabinet minister of the party in power who held the agricultural portfolio, with a farmer as his deputy. During my eight year tenure in this role, I was deputy to two cabinet ministers. Often at a moments notice the minister would be called to the house for a vote or to make a statement: my role was a very collaborative one, being ready to stand in as the need arose. And before a committee, being ready and able to provide him with a practical briefing.

My appointment to serve as Welsh Commissioner on the Meat and Livestock Commission came about in 1973, a term of duty which lasted 13 years, during 8 of which I chaired their Sheep Advisory Committee and for a time the Pigs Committee. This was a challenging role, because farmers representation on the MLC was low (2 farmer commissioners) even though it relied heavily on farmers livestock levy for finance. Its remit covered from 'conception to consumption' with a powerful representation from the butchery trade and supermarket directors. Livestock breeding with visits to bull testing stations, and advising the Ministry of Agriculture, featured strongly in our work. Even though farmers obviously provided a high vested interest in livestock breeding and production, our minority role meant that our points of view had to be put over forcefully and with clarity. Additionally it was made very clear to me that membership of the MLC would mean forsaking my connection with membership of the NFU London committees. This was to ensure that in my dealings with farmers, my representation was even handed, whatever union or none the farmer belonged to. This I was able to do across all allegiances. I found it very fulfilling to be able to present the Welsh farming point of view squarely to the people who mattered.'

The Welsh Halfbred Sheep Breeders Association, first formally established in 1955, now has a membership of 354 and continues its annual sales of ewes. There are five in all held during September and early October at Builth Wells, Welshpool, and at Ruthin in north Wales, which is still the main producing area. The year 2005 marks the fiftieth anniversary of founding the Welsh Halfbred Sheep Breeders Association and to celebrate this occasion the three surviving founder members, Gordon Wilyman, Nick Archdale and Francis Morris are to receive joint presidency for that year.

The General Secretary is Gill Napper (telephone 01691 860 336) of Bryn Teg, Pen y Garnedd, Llanrhaeadr-ym-Mochnant, Powys. SY10 0AW.

Part II

Chapter 4

Gordon Wilyman: Facing the Melai Challenge

Bob Hughes, nine years younger than Gordon Wilyman, had first come to Melai as a shepherd in 1944 to work for the Moores family. The Moores were Liverpool business people who had established the Littlewoods Football Pools and Mail Order company and a member of the family, Arthur Moores, had married a Melai daughter.

So from his farm upbringing at nearby Tan y Bodran, immersed in sheep farming from childhood, Bob had come to Melai as a twenty year old. He had later worked for Shadrach Davies, a subsequent owner, before Edward Owen and Gordon Wilyman took over in 1950.

In writing about Gordon Wilyman there is an ever recurring puzzle: how could a man who, by his own admission, knew nothing at all about sheep and hill farming make such an outstanding success of an upland farm like Melai? And how did he, a Brummie, fit into and become so well accepted in the depths of rural Wales?

Perhaps as our story progresses there will be pointers, what is certain is that Gordon Wilyman was no ordinary farmer and certainly no ordinary man.

Gordon Wilyman and Bob Hughes became close friends from the start. Mr Wilyman pays him this tribute: 'Bob has been my tutor from the beginning and I couldn't have had a better one'. Bob responds by saying that Gordon Wilyman was a quick learner. That is a reflection on the skills of both, because Mr Wilyman rapidly put into effect at Melai all that he absorbed from Bob Hughes, together with the organizational skills he had acquired on farms since leaving Birmingham.

Bob and Gordon are still firm friends, and in fact two of Bob's nephews (his sister's sons), Gwyndaf and Arwel Owen joined the working team at Melai: Gwyndaf in 1968 and Arwel about 3 years later. And were still there when Melai was sold in 2002, which is testimony to a great working relationship.

Bob well remembers Gordon's arrival at Melai with his little grey 'Fergie' tractor and trailer which he had driven from Ewloe. Gordon recalls that he had agreed to take on Melai before his wife Winnie had even seen the house. This was because on the day of the proposed visit she had gone into labour with their second son Roger, so that other arrangements had to be made !

And even when wife and young family moved in, in September 1950, there was the further difficulty that Shadrach Davies, the previous owner and his family had not had possession of Bodrochwyn Ganol, the holding to which they in turn were moving. So, by agreement, the Davies family stayed in part of the house for about three months. 'We got on surprisingly well,' says Gordon, and a close bond was formed between them, with baby Roger and six year old John getting a whole lot of fuss from an extended family!

Added to that there was a great deal of work to be done on the house, which had been neglected; Gordon Wilyman recalls that conditions were quite primitive: electric light was provided by a bank of batteries – ex war surplus – which had been left there since Arthur Moores' time. These had to be regularly charged up via belt and pulley, driven by the little Fergie tractor, to provide a basic 110 volts which was suitable for lighting only. There was piped water from a spring in a nearby field, which dried up completely in dry summers and froze up in hard winters. 'On those occasions we had to fetch house water in churns from the Crossley's at Hendre Llwyn-y-Maen about a mile away,' says Mr Wilyman.

After about two years Gordon installed a Lister Start-o-matic plant to provide a better electricity supply, which generated 220 volts. That was still some time before a mains connection for water and electricity came about in the early sixties.

The farmstead had a good set of stall accommodation for cattle, and over the old coach-house there was a bell tower with a boar's head crest of the Newborough dynasty, a reminder of the time when Melai was the home farm on the estate. The field fencing was fairly good but neglect of land management showed a need for a high application of lime to combat soil acidity.

There were other buildings here, remnants from when Melai was once the centre of a township. A laundry shed appropriately near Nant Melai (the rivulet which rises in the Hiraethog mountain above Llansannan and flows through the farm) became accommodation for Gordon's ten sow pig enterprise. Much later this was demolished: the slates and stones used to renovate the farmstead. Added to that its proximity to the watercourse and disposal of the pig effluent, finally resolved its destiny!

A pigeon-house (colomendy) in a state of dereliction indicated a time when Melai had once a source of pigeon meat for the family, as well as a stock of carrier pigeons to convey messages back home when they went away to visit friends. This Gordon also dismantled, using the stone to update the main farmstead, and later utilizing the base as a foundation for a bungalow where he now lives.

A water mill which ceased its normal function since the war, existed a quarter mile upstream. This too was used for pig housing before its purchase and renovation as a holiday home by Robin Ibbs (now Sir Robin Ibbs), a director of ICI and a member of Mrs Margaret Thatcher's Think Tank. The mill leat had driven an electricity turbine very early on for a neighbour William Wynne of Bryn Ynyr who, self taught, went on to construct his own television set, one of the first in the area.

Horses were still in vogue at Melai. Edward Owen who partnered Gordon here for the first three years was an acknowledged expert. He found a sound horse for Bob Hughes to shepherd the Melai flock, as well as suitable horses for general farm work.

But it was the little grey Fergie which Gordon had driven from Buckley that was the mainstay. Fergusons proved invaluable, it was a make which he held on to throughout his time at Melai. Fairly early on Edward Thomas, the International tractor agent at Denbigh, tried to persuade him to change, which resulted in a challenge. A ploughing test between a little grey Ferguson, provided by North Wales Engineers of St Asaph, and an International from Edward Thomas was arranged on one of Melai's steep slopes. It proved to be a no contest: the International reared its front end up in the air in a forlorn effort, while the Ferguson ploughed away sweetly with little effort, proving the worth of Harry Ferguson's unique three point linkage!

Corn was grown at Melai intermittently up to the 1990's providing straw and grain for the livestock – but by then this was the only place for miles around which did so. And how the crows knew it!

In the early years the threshing outfit run by Tom Roberts of Llanfair Talhaearn, comprising of a Ransom threshing box, Jones stationary baler, and an Oliver 90 TVO tractor, which drove the lot was a standard winter caller. This gave way to the bagger combine harvester operated by Tudor Williams of Pen Isaf Llangernyw, and later to the tanker machine of Tudor Davies, Glan Gors, Llanfair Talhaearn. This meant a lot less work, not only around the corn ricks at harvest and threshing time, when extra men were needed, but also domestically for Winnie who provided the obligatory mid day and supper feasts for both the threshing and shearing gangs.

Milking about forty cows was a feature at Melai, at first within a shippon system, converting in 1960 to a Simplex Abreast Parlour and loose housing. By 1968, when John, Gordon's eldest son had completed his education and was home on the farm a decision was taken to change the farm policy. This meant disposing of the dairy enterprise in favour of a purely sheep, cattle suckler and beef system. This allowed for mixed grazing on the top land, with the lowland becoming a source of early grass for the mothering ewes.

The grazing rights for 350 sheep, 6 miles away on Mynydd Hiraethog (Denbigh Moors) taken on with Melai in 1950, were now discontinued. Distance and shepherding had made it less practical. At first shearing with hand clippers, after the sheep had been washed in a dammed rivulet on the moors, by a large assembly of local workers, later evolved, in two or three years, into a mechanical operation with shearing machines driven by petrol motors. It had all became less feasible with its reliance on fine weather, and the carting of equipment and adequate food to keep the squad going.

By 1968 Gordon's eldest son John was shouldering more responsibility. His education had progressed from the local village school at Llanfair Talhaearn to the Secondary Modern School at Abergele. Then on to Brookland Hall a boarding school for boys at Welshpool. A year as a boarder at Llyfasi College of Agriculture doing General Farm Studies followed, supplemented by a further two years on a day release Farm Business Management course.

John and Gordon were alike in many ways, always immaculate in appearance and precise in their opinions. He had inherited much of Gordon's analytical skills and was confident in farming committees. It was customary for both to do an overview of the farm livestock together before breakfast, which provided the opportunity for a discussion on farm policy, as well as doing the more mundane chores endemic in country life.

At farmers union meetings he showed the same quality of leadership and authority which featured strongly in Gordon's personae. He had the same analytical thought processes, fellow farmers deferred to his opinion. Little wonder then, that his path in the public domain in many ways paralleled that of his father, some twenty years earlier. The chair of the local

Abergele NFU was quickly followed by that of the Clwyd County branch in 1992, and inevitably becoming the County representative in London on the NFU HQ Livestock Committee. No organisation could be better represented. Like his father, John was a hands on farmer and committee man, and as with his father, knowing where to draw the line between practical farm work and decision making, and strenuously representing his farmer kinsmen in the corridors of power. The balance was finely drawn. Later John became the Welsh Commissioner on the MLC, a role played with distinction by his father for 13 years some 20 years earlier.

But we are getting ahead of ourselves: back in 1968 for John Wilyman there was a career role alongside Gordon to forge. There can be no doubt that this was to refine his farming promise. Gradually Gordon could ease off: in 1973 his stint as MLC Welsh Commissioner meant leaving the farm for longer periods, which allowed for greater delegation.

Chapter 5

Addressing the Oxford Farming Conference

Gordon was now firmly centre stage on the UK farming scene: in January 1973 addressing the prestigious Oxford Farming Conference on 'The Challenges Facing the British Hill farmer in the European Common Market'. There, to an assembly of 600 people at the Oxford Town Hall, he was to crystallize what he had accomplished in the twenty years since he took over at Melai on his own account. After some preliminaries, he set out his stall by telling the assemblage about Melai:

'Melai is situated in the fairly kind uplands of northern Wales, midway between the coast and the Snowdonian Mountain Range, an area of fairly high rainfall averaging slightly over fifty inches a year, most of it falling in the late autumn, winter and early spring. The total acreage is 630 ranging in height from about 550 to just over 1100 ft above sea level. A breakdown of the acreage would show about 120 acres of reasonably flat meadow land which overlies a gravel sub-soil and is therefore free draining, 140 acres of sound upland, most of which is quite steeply undulating providing good shelter for stock, 290 acres of hill land in the 900 to 1100 ft contours, a good deal of it in steep banks with outcrops of rocks, and finally, 70 acres of steep scrub woodland.'

Here in his own words we savour the occasion as well as appreciate the measure of the challenges he faced.

Gordon Wilyman continued:

'In 1952 about 80 acres of the lower land had been in continuous corn crops for a number of years and was sadly in need of re-seeding, a large proportion of the top land was quite unproductive, growing little else but bracken. The previous owner who had only been in occupation for about five years had not been in a position to make any substantial improvements.

The stock on the farm at this time was about 90 head of cattle, a flock of 800 Welsh mountain ewes and 16 Welsh pony mares. Large hill farms in Wales were not in great demand in the 1950's and the purchase price was in the region of £45 per acre.

At this time in addition to the farm there were grazing rights for about 350 Welsh ewes on some Crown land about six miles distant from the farm, this was on a stretch of unfenced wet and windswept moorland about 1600ft up and covering several thousand acres, it was quite inaccessible to any wheeled vehicles and the vegetation was chiefly nardus and sphagnum moss. It was only capable of supporting a very small type of Welsh Mountain ewe from early May to the end of September, for the rest of the year they had to be kept on the farm. Although the land was wet and boggy the sheep never suffered from either fluke or foot rot, the acid condition of the black peaty soil was an unsuitable habitat for the small water snail which is host to the Fluke worm, or the foot rot organism. Improving the land was out of the question because of the difficulty of access, and in 1960 I decided to sell the Mountain Flock and with it went the grazing rights, a decision I have never regretted. We now keep in its place a much larger type of Welsh ewe suitable for crossing, which gives us a far better return. Taking stock of the situation when I first moved into the farm, I could see that the challenge for me was to make a living for myself and a young family from 600 acres of rather inherently poor land, in a fairly low state of fertility, with the additional handicap of a large mortgage. The financial returns from either beef breeding or feeding at that time were extremely low, and it appeared that milk production was my only hope, although the farm was not ideally suited to dairying, and the buildings were old fashioned and laborious to work.

I established a dairy herd of Friesian cattle and remained in milk production until 1967: during this period improvements were made to some of the hill land, the ewe flock was increased and buildings were brought into line with modern standards. By this time beef breeding had become a far more attractive proposition and the prospects looked even brighter with the likelihood of our joining the Common Market and the revised line for Hill Sheep and Hill Cows meant that I was eligible to draw subsidy on a greater number of animals. Taking these points into consideration and after talking things over with my son who by this time was at home with me, we decided to change over from dairying to a single suckled beef herd. One other deciding factor was that we felt that we should be better able to improve and utilize our top land by mixed stocking with cattle and sheep rather than grazing mainly with sheep plus a few of the young stock from the dairy herd.

Having decided on a plan we then proceeded to put it into operation, the dairy cows were sold off as they came to calve, and in the autumn I went up to Northumberland and bought sixty Blue Grey in-calf heifers all due to calve before the end of the year: this started off our suckler herd. By this time we had an all grass farm having re-seeded all the arable land, and since then have only ploughed for catch crops and re-seeding, but over the previous fifteen years we had ploughed, cropped with rape and re-seeded most of the hill land that could be reasonably be tackled with wheeled tractors. In common with most of the land in this fairly high rainfall area soil samples showed that the pH value was low and acidity high, requiring in some cases as much as 5 tons of ground limestone to correct it. There is a continuous need for the application of phosphates which we believe can most effectively be applied in the form of basic slag: there is a reasonably high natural potash content. The fertilizer policy for the whole farm has been to lime to counteract any acidity, to apply 10 cwt per acre of 16% slag on a third of the farm each year and to give dressings of potash only to land which is to be cut for hay or silage. Nitrogen is applied mainly in two dressings of 55 units each, one in spring to encourage some early grass and one in the autumn to promote some winter keep, additional dressings of about 100 units are given to fields which are to be shut up for cutting for either hay or silage.

There is a great deal of the hill land of Wales that could be brought into a higher state of fertility if only it were more accessible. Quite a large proportion of our land from 900 to 1,000 feet up is reasonably flat but the approach fields are very steep, making it impossible to get up with a tractor and trailer with loads of more than 15 cwt to 1 ton, and this can only be done under favourable weather conditions. By taking advantage of Hill Land Improvement grants we have been able to construct rough hard core roads, and as a result we are now able to get up with loads of 50 cwts under most weather conditions, and bulk spreaders carrying lime and slag can get to the top. The modern tractor fitted with improved hydraulics and a differential lock have been a wonderful aid to the safer working of steep hill land.

The next important step was to tackle the very top land, the unploughable areas of the farm, and over the last four years we have carried out a programme of surface treatment which has given outstanding results. The method is simply to cut with a Howard flail mower, top dress with lime, slag and nitrogen and encourage stock to graze it. After one season there is a marked improvement and after three, a sward containing ryegrass, cocksfoot and clover where little else but gorse and bracken grew before. It is pointless encouraging the growth of grass without having the stock to consume it either growing or conserved. The grazing stock carried at the present time is 100 breeding cows, 130 head of young stock and 1,500 breeding ewes, the stocking density of the farm in 1952 was 2.7 acres per cow equivalent; in 1967, 2.2 and in 1972, 1.6.

The system of improvement is not quite as simple as I have outlined but the results on land growing heavy crops of bracken have far exceeded our expectations. To be really effective the cutting has to be carried out twice a year, in June when the bracken fronds are at a tender stage, and again in the autumn. We are now trying to get a faster rate of improvement by scarifying the surface of the treated land, sowing clover seed in the early spring and treading it in by feeding sheep on those areas. We consider that one of the most important operations in the management of upland pastures is to pasture top in the late summer to get rid of thistles and weeds before they seed, and also to cut off all the old seeded grass so that young growth can take its place, we do this every year immediately after hay harvest, but before we put on the autumn dressing of nitrogen.

Two separate suckler herds are maintained – an autumn calving herd of about 70 Blue Greys calving mainly in October and November which are brought into yards in November and housed for the winter, the cows are fed on self feed silage with no additional concentrates, but the calves have access to a creep area where they get hay ad lib, and up to three pounds of barley and beet pulp a day. The cows and calves are turned out on the hill land in the spring and graze there throughout the summer. The calves are weaned at the beginning of August and turned on to silage aftermath to graze until about mid-October; they are then brought into yards for feeding and go off during the winter at about 15 months old.

The spring calving herd of about 30 mainly Welsh Blacks are run on a lower cost system; they are out wintered on a block of land containing about 20 acres of scrub wood which gives them a good shelter, a dry bed and a clean place to feed. From Christmas onwards they are fed on hay and self help urea protein blocks, they calve out in March and early April.

When there is sufficient growth of grass they go back up on the hill land where they graze until the end of October. The calves are then weaned and kept in sheds on just a store ration for the winter, and finished out on grass the following summer at about 18 months old. The bulls used on both herds are a ¾ bred Charolais and a South Devon.

I suppose that over the years the Hereford would be regarded as the traditional bull used in beef suckler herds, and the Hereford Friesian cross has proved to be an excellent suckler cow, but we have found that using a Hereford bull on our Blue Grey and Welsh Black cows produces a calf that is easy to feed but lacking in growth potential for the heavier weight cattle now in demand, in fact the heifer calves reached a weight of 6 to 7 cwts and afterwards just put on fat. The Charolais/Friesian cross and the South Devon bulls produce calves that can be run on to heavier weights and still retain a lean carcass.

The sheep flock of 1,500 are all Welsh Mountain ewes which are put to Border Leicester rams to produce the Welsh Halfbred lambs. The ewes are bought in at draft sales from mountain farms mainly as four year olds – we keep them for an average of three crops of lambs which means that about 1/3rd of the flock is replaced each year. When we have finished with them the majority are still good enough in their mouths to be sold as draft ewes again, going down to Vale farmers who are able to get another two lamb crops from them.

The Halfbred ewe lambs are sold as breeding lambs during the first week in September each year at the north Wales sale organized by the Welsh Halfbred Sheep Breeders Association, where they make considerably more than fat lamb prices. The tup lambs are entirely grass fed and are all graded, going away in batches from the end of June until the beginning of December, most of them are sold to a local firm of meat wholesalers to kill out at weights from 36 to 40 lbs, and are very much of the type and quality that his butcher customers demand.

The Welsh Halfbred Sheep Breeders Association has proved to be one of the successful ventures into co-operative marketing in Wales, and I am proud to be one of its founder members. The Association was first started some 16 years ago, and in the first year about 3,200 breeding sheep were sold, in recent years as many as 50,000 sheep have been sold in a season. We have the full support of three firms of auctioneers and this has been a major contribution to the success of the three sales sponsored by the Association each year. When we first started this venture we were not promoting a new breed, some farmers had been using Border Leicester rams on Welsh ewes for many years before, but we set out to establish three centres where buyers would know that they would be able to see several thousand ewes and lambs of a uniform type and quality. Only members of the association can enter sheep for the sales and a panel of inspectors are appointed whose job is to inspect all the pens before the sale commences and cull out any undesirable types. We do our best to give buyers confidence in the sale by giving guarantees of soundness of teeth, feet and udders and freedom from certain diseases.

We claim that the Welsh Halfbred ewe is an ideal animal for commercial fat lamb production, she combines the qualities of hardiness, longevity, ability to milk and the wonderful mothering instinct of the Welsh ewe, with the growth and bold character of the Border Leicester. Our sheep are now in most of the counties of England and in recent years some have crossed the border into Scotland. Finances for publicity and sales promotion are raised by a small levy on all sheep sold at the sales. This co-operative venture benefits the upland farmer who breeds the Halfbreds and also stimulates the trade of the draft Welsh ewes from the mountain farms.

The farm is run with a total labour force of four men: a shepherd, a general stockman-cum-tractor driver, my son and myself. Contractors are employed for such jobs as shearing, hay baling, spreading slag and lime and other work at key periods. In addition to the grazing livestock a small pig unit enables us to utilize some of the older buildings after doing cheap

King Edward's School, New Street, Birmingham which Gordon Wilyman attended after leaving Aston Grammar School.

Gordon and Winnie Wilyman at their wedding on Ocober 21, 1939.

The Colomendy (Pigeon House) at Melai in 1950.

Sheep Shearing – 1952. Pictured (left to right) Mrs Edward Owen; Mrs Gordon Wilyman; John Wilyman (kneeling); Back row: William Jones (Llansannan); William Pearce, Hafod y Gaer; Rev. C. Gwyn Jones, St Asaph; Edward Owen; Gwil Davies, Cornwal Isa (the mountain shepherd); John Jones, Bedwyn Isa; John Foulkes, Botrual Isa; John Hughes, Tan y Bodran; Wil Davies, Tan Graig; Abrams, Tŷ Du; Bob Davies, Hafod Lom; Edwin Roberts, Foel, Llansannan; Bob Hughes, Oswald Jones, Llanfair; David Williams, Tŷ Newydd.

Gordon Wilyman does a radio interview about the Welsh Halfbreds.
On the occasion of a 'Conference and Demonstration: A case for sheep on the
mixed farm' held at The Royal Agricultural College Cirencester in conjunction
with the Welsh Halfbred Sheep Breeders Association (May 14, 1974).

Trefor Roberts, Pengwern Hall, Llangollen and Francis Morris leading breeders of Welsh Halfbreds at the 'Conference and Sheep Demonstration' held at the Royal Agricultural College, Cirencester on May 14, 1974.

The Welsh Halfbred ewe shows her worth for crossing on the lowlands.

An open day at Melai. Instantly recognizable are some leading NFU people. To Gordon's right, A.E. Jones, Llangernyw while to the left, J.T. Richardson Jones and Sir (now Lord) Henry Plumb.

At home 1976: Gordon Wilyman, Mollie Hughes, Dilys Mars Jones, Mabel Lloyd Hughes, Winifred Wilyman and David Mars Jones (Mayor of Colwyn).

Mr and Mrs Gordon Wilyman photographed on the occasion of his receiving the OBE from Her Majesty the Queen at Buckingham Palace in 1979, with their sons Roger (left) and John.

Gordon Wilyman receiving the 'Farm Buildings Award' for his sheep handling shed at Melai from Gwyn Hughes of Denbigh, President of the Royal Welsh Show, July 1981.

Deep in conversation: Gordon Wilyman, MLC Welsh Commissioner left and MLC Chairman, David Samworth exchange views with the chairman of Barclays Bank and Keith Roberts, Deputy Chairman of MLC at the Royal Welsh Show 1984.

Winifred Wilyman receiving the John Hooson Cup for farm conservation from Menna Owen at the Flint and Denbigh Show August 1988. Also pictured: Mr and Mrs Bob Edwards (Chair and Consort of Clwyd County Council), Iola Jones, Meurig Owen (Chairman Denbighshire County Branch NFU), Stephen Darlington and Dick Hughes (NFU County Secretary).

Nick Archdale and Gordon Wilyman at the Welsh Halfbred Sheep Sale at Ruthin (September 1993).

NFU President David Naish met Denbighshire farmers at Melai during John Wilyman's Chairmanship of the Clwyd County Branch in 1992. Around the table left to right: John Wilyman, Dewi Jones (secretary Llansannan YFC), Mrs Margaret Wilyman, David Naish, David Edwards (Llanrwst NFU) Arwyn Davies (NFU Group Secretary), Keith Jones (NFU Public Affairs Officer), Bill Goldsworthy NFU Welsh Director and Gwyn Hughes (vice chairman Betws-yn-rhos YFC)

Prime Minister John Major on a fact finding mission to Melai – October 1992: left to right: David Hunt MP, Secretary of State for Wales; James Wilyman, Roger Wilyman, Gaynor Wilyman, Gordon Wilyman, Winifred Wilyman, John Major, John Wilyman, Margaret Wilyman, Daniel Wilyman. Standing in front of John Major, Richard Wilyman.

John Major and John Wilyman in discussion. On the left David Hunt, and on the right of the picture Gordon Wilyman.

Daniel and James (John Wilyman's sons) with John Major. Foreground,
Richard (Roger Wilyman's son). Pictured on Ffrith Bedwyn Melai,
1100 feet above sea level.

David Hunt, John Major and
Gordon Wilyman at Melai 1992

Winnie, Gordon and Honey,
Gordon's gun dog (1994).

Five prominent Welsh Halfbred Sheep Breeders received commemorative crooks to mark the Association's fortieth anniversary at Sheep 95 at Melai (1995). Left to right: Gordon Wilyman, Nick Archdale, Francis Morris, Owen Price (founder members), and Tom Rowlands.

John and Gordon Wilyman at Sheep 95 (Melai 1995).

*Pictured at Sheep 95 Wales – May 16, 1995 at Melai. Left to right:
Alun Evans, Gordon Wilyman, Winnie, Roger and John Wilyman and
Gareth Evans.*

Part of the 4000 people at Sheep 95 Wales held at Melai

Gordon, Roger and Winnie at Sheep 95 Wales.

Sheep 95 Wales drew a large crowd from all parts of the country to Melai.

Cause for celebration at Sheep 95 Wales – Melai (May 1995). Left to right: Roger, Winnie, Gordon, Margaret (John's wife) and John Wilyman.

Inside the lambing shed at Melai – Sheep 95.

David Lowe, Iona Jones and Roger Wilyman at Sheep 95 Wales.

A lot to see and talk about in the main marquee at Sheep 95 Wales (Melai, May 1995).

Firm friends: Bob Hughes the Melai shepherd and Gordon Wilyman photographed in July 2003.

Nick Archdale and Gordon Wilyman in jovial mood recalling the Welsh Halfbred pioneering days. Picture taken in July 2003.

conversions, and also keeps the regular labour force fully employed.

Weaner pigs are bought in from a Group at about 50lbs live weight and are fed through to heavy cutters which are sold to our local meat firm. Our throughput is about 1,500 pigs a year. These occupy only a quarter of a man's time, and show a useful financial return on capital investment.

Our pig enterprise is the one part of our farming system that I have not a great deal of confidence in under EEC market conditions, and although it is a useful sideline, the amount of capital we have put into it is small, and it could quickly be phased out should it become unprofitable.

Up to this point I have merely had to set down events that have taken place: from here on I have to make an attempt at gazing into the crystal ball and see in it the changing conditions that we will have to face following upon our entry into Europe.

For at least the next decade I have every confidence in the prospects of the livestock farmer and especially for those maintaining breeding herds of cattle and flocks of sheep.

The reduction of imports from the Commonwealth and possibly from Ireland will leave a gap in the home market that will not easily be filled on account of the world shortage of all meat products and of beef in particular. The British government appears to realise the need to encourage increased meat production from the agricultural industry to help counteract new pressures on our balance of payments which are expected to follow our entry into the EEC. Having made these points I would add that on no account does this mean that we should allow ourselves to be lulled into a feeling of complacency, there is a real challenge and we must face up to it in a tough and realistic manner.

I believe that the changes we have made in our farming system over the last six years are bringing it nearer to fitting the pattern best suited to meet the market requirement in the EEC. By exploiting to the full the good growth of grass that can be obtained in the wetter areas of west Wales we are endeavouring to develop a moderately low cost enterprise with a high output. While we feel that at two and a half ewes per acre the sheep stocking is somewhere near the optimum level, we plan to increase the cow numbers by draining some wet sections on the top land and further improvements to grassland. It is becoming increasingly evident that the market trend is for heavier weight cattle that are not over fat, the lightweight steer no longer commands a premium. We are meeting this requirement by the use of bulls that produce calves with this potential and intend to carry our cattle on for a longer period. When calf prices are high it is an advantage to spread the initial cost over a greater number of pounds of beef in the finished animal.

Plans for increasing the returns from the ewe flock include aiming at a higher lambing percentage, carrying lambs through to heavier weights by growing catch crops such as the direct drilling of swedes and turnips, this would also avoid selling lambs in the glut periods of September and October when market prices are at their lowest.

I must point out that the success of any livestock enterprise is dependant to a great extent on the quality of the labour available. We are very fortunate to have top quality men: if we are to retain them, working conditions must be improved and the drudgery of laborious chores cut down to a minimum. With this in view, we have in recent years erected a shed over the sheep handling pens and installed a spray race where 20 sheep can be sprayed at a time; this takes the place of the old dipping bath. We are now discussing the merits of building a lambing shed to hold 600 ewes and the further development of the batch lambing system by the greater use of vasectomised rams.

Having adopted the techniques I have outlined I feel confident that we shall be in a much stronger position to face up to the challenges of the next few years. In my opinion the advances made by the British livestock farmer have placed him in a stronger position to compete favourably with any new competition he may be called upon to face.'

As with all Oxford Farming Conference sessions there followed the inevitable discussion where the main speakers are held to account. Here Mr Wilyman was able to elaborate on the Melai system. Clearly farmers held their breath fearing the unknown factors awaiting them in the European Common Market. Farming was at a cross roads; what was to happen to government support for agriculture? How would the farmer on the so called marginal land fare? Would the grants for land improvement continue? Mr Wilyman felt, at least where Melai was concerned, that the future was safe. He had capitalized on the Hill Land schemes offered by the Ministry in the 1950/70 period – schemes for field drainage, reseeding, and hardcore tracks to access his top land had been readily taken up to great advantage. It meant that Melai land could be better serviced in every way. While the lowland meadows provided a good source of winter pasture. Lambs and beef cattle could now be finished there, rather than be sold prematurely as stores for finishing elsewhere.

Further, he saw Melai as a source of sheep breeding stock for the lowland farmer via the hybrid Welsh Halfbred which he had so famously promoted.

His ideas on suckler beef too were well noted at Oxford. His use of a three quarter Charolais bull on Blue Grey cows made for an easy calving regime and produced larger framed finished cattle for the meat trade, he argued. This evidently surprised his listeners, but he reasoned that a suckler cow system differed from that of dairying in as much that steaming up for high milk production was not a requirement.

Melai was a template that others could well emulate.

It's a remarkable fact that the first twenty years at Melai were Gordon Wilyman's most dynamic: not only had he transformed the farm into what was essentially a national showcase, he had at the same time become heavily involved through various committees in influencing, at the upper reaches, government farming policy. And all this had been achieved from a low baseline start, fraught with financial worries.

His close friend Meuric Rees of Towyn, in west Wales, who in many ways shares his entrepreneurial stance and followed Gordon as Welsh MLC Commissioner, says that Gordon was able to compartmentalize his committee interests. 'He knew where to draw the line: never allowing committee work to jeopardize his farming.'

'So often we find people becoming professional committee men, and in that way allowing their farms to became adversely affected.' With Gordon Wilyman this never happened: it tells a lot about his energy and commitment that usually his day included time for both his farm as well as sessions at such places as Aberystwyth and even further afield. Indeed it is evident that in the cut and thrust of these committees he was able to glean ideas which he was able to profitably apply at Melai.

Meuric Rees' friendship grew with a shared interest in livestock: both farmed hill land, although some of Rees' land went to an even higher altitude than Melai. 'Mr Wilyman has an inborn gift as a stockman,' he says, 'and that is something that you can never learn from books.'

As to his qualities as a committee man again Mr Rees is fulsome in his admiration. 'As a chairman he allowed everyone to have their say but he always kept them to what was relevant to the agenda. He listened carefully and summarized conclusions with consummate skill.'

He also has the gift of being able to get on well with people which is another important committee factor. But Mr Rees says that, 'as far as his public speaking ability is concerned he is not an orator with the ability to move audiences to a frenzy; rather his style is direct, and his appeal through reasoned argument commands public attention.' Turning to his farming skills

Meuric Rees pays tribute to Gordon's analytical ability: 'with forensic thoroughness he can adeptly judge the feasibility of a course of farming activity. But contrary to the practice of many farmers, he makes time for holidays: for many, traditionally, a day at the market fulfilled the "time off" requirement. This was not so for Mr Wilyman who believes in the holiday edict. Even though that meant organization and delegation, he would arrange a fortnight or three weeks away from the farm.'

Meuric Rees believes that the fact of Gordon's urban background worked to his advantage because it meant, using the modern term, that he had no baggage. In other words he was not hidebound by tradition and was therefore ready and willing to accept new ideas.

John Hooson also a former Oxford Farming Conference speaker, a one time chairman of the powerful NFU Parliamentary Committee in London, has vivid recollections of Gordon's skill as a committee man. 'He was often the farmers first choice as a chairman with a reputation for evenhandedness and where a degree of fair play and trust was required.' John Hooson remembers being a co-delegate with Iorwerth Jones and Gordon Wilyman to the first meeting of the NFU Welsh Council which was set up to offset the influence of the fledgling FUW. Feelings ran high at that time with a fair amount of bitterness emanating: Gordon was the man who people on both sides of the divide could talk to. John uses a Welsh expression to describe him, 'Gordon is a *gŵr bonheddig*', he says. It's a term not easily translated, it refers to a gentleman whom others hold in high regard and respect.

Elfed Williams the NFU Group Secretary at Llanrwst and Uwchaled is another who holds Gordon in high regard. His career with the NFU began in 1964 during Mr Wilyman's term as chairman of the Denbighshire County Branch. His view is unequivocal: 'Gordon Wilyman was an excellent chairman who progressed meetings in an even-handed way. With him every word counted and was listened to. Whatever he said carried weight and was respected. And when he later became a commissioner on the Meat and Livestock Commission, all farmers could be assured of a sympathetic hearing from him – whether they were members of the NFU, FUW or whatever.'

Another who shares much of Gordon Wilyman's philosophy is Captain Nick Archdale. That is a friendship which dates back to when Rhodesian-born Nick Archdale first came to Penbedw near Mold fresh from an army commission. Gordon was at the Buckley pig farm then and might easily have taken on Penbedw Ucha an upland holding on the estate when the farm became vacant at that time. However destiny defined a different course and Melai was the result.

Remarkably both are gifted stockmen, regardless of their backgrounds! Archdale's tuition came at the feet of Miss Buddicombe, his sister's godmother, a close family friend, owner of the Penbedw estate, who was a farmer of high repute. But she gave him no favours, save granting the tenancy of Penbedw on a market value rental. Like Gordon Wilyman, Archdale had 'no baggage' but he had the quality of stockmanship to a high order. It was a friendship which was ultimately to forge the formation of the Welsh Halfbred Association. They were the leading young Turks who were to define its destiny. Archdale is adamant about Wilyman's profound contribution: 'He gave the Association the stamp of integrity,' he says.

Chapter 6

Gordon Wilyman and his family

It may come as a surprise to learn that Gordon Wilyman has a love of the sea. From early farming days at Buckley, this was an interest he shared with his friend John Davies of Cop House Farm Saltney, who had a boat at Conwy. This as it happens was an interest later taken up by both his sons John and Roger who raced Fireball dinghies at Rhos on Sea with the Colwyn Bay Sailing Club (which was where John was to meet and later, in 1978, marry Margaret Reynolds whose father had a hairdressing business there). A cursory look into the Wilyman ancestry may explain where the call of the sea originated.

We find that Gordon's grandfather, Thomas Wilyman, one of a large family, went to sea and served as a twelve year old cabin boy on the Cutty Sark which was a tea clipper in those days. Later, home from the sea, he operated as a fisherman in Sutton on Sea and for many years served as a Lifeboat Coxswain there. This was on the notoriously treacherous North Sea coastline when lifeboats relied on brave and courageous oarsmen, before the days of motorized vessels. And when called out into the storm, the lifeboat was drawn down the foreshore with a team of four horses.

But as every nice girl loves a sailor grandfather Wilyman, romanced and married the daughter of a local firm of farming auctioneers. This incurred family disapproval, because they believed she had married well below her station, and they cut her off without a penny. When they married he could neither read nor write, and it was left to his bride to teach him to read the Bible and to write. But in spite of his hard life, Gordon remembers his grandfather as an extremely kind hearted person. Thus is recorded a fragment of Wilyman antecedents, in many ways unconventional if not unique.

There are only 30 or so Wilyman names listed in the entire

UK telephone directory and it is believed that the name is of Flemish or Danish origin.

Gordon's father, having survived the Great War in the trenches of France returned to civilian life to find that his former employer was a casualty of the war, and that his job as agent on a private estate had gone. He then became financial advisor to W. & T. Avery at Walsal near Birmingham (having first joined the company as a clerk). On his retirement at 65, he took over a moulding works on his own account at their trading estate making weighbridge castings. In fact Wilyman senior was actively running a business until he was 92 and died in his late nineties in 1985. 'He was quite a determined character with a modern outlook who always enjoyed being with younger people,' Roger Wilyman observes.

We have in an earlier chapter followed Gordon Wilyman's remarkable career ladder.

From Birmingham's City centre and against strenuous family advice, setting his sights on a farming dream which was to receive the ultimate accolade at Melai with an OBE award in 1979 from her Majesty the Queen, for services to agriculture. And in 1985, on the nomination of the Royal Welsh Agricultural Society, awarded a Fellowship of the Royal Agricultural Societies for his services to Welsh Agriculture.

But along the way Gordon Wilyman showed how true is the old adage, 'that you make more opportunities than you find'. And that must be attributed largely to his ability to get on with people.

From his days as a raw youngster on farms, Chester YFC (where he learnt more than he'll readily admit), Rease Heath College and later in 1939 his marriage to Winnie, this was evidently so. This latter event was the corner stone of his success. She was the eldest of four children, two girls and two boys, of a Cheshire farming family. But the match didn't have the appropriation of his in-laws. Marriage to a struggling Buckley pig farmer was not what they wanted for their daughter. But it is evident that as a marriage this was heaven made. In relating his life story Mr Wilyman keeps coming back with fulsome praise for his soul mate. There is a saying that says, 'love flies out of the window when poverty knocks on the door', and when they first came to Melai they most certainly faced severe financial difficulties. But there, with two very young children in tow, Winnie worked hard even though money was tight. She created a home, transforming the garden over run with nettles and dilapidated hen huts into a haven of colour; and with her sister Marjorie (thirteen years younger than she was) cleaning up and re-decorating a house which had suffered from years of neglect. Added to that there were two farm men who lived on the premises to feed and care for.

Winnie was a first rate cook and seamstress who could run up all her own clothes. Above all Mrs Wilyman, whose presence would grace any occasion, could give moral encouragement and support to her husband and was an exemplar mother to their children.

Their eldest son John was born on March 8th, 1944 when they were still at Buckley. It was while there that he started attending kindergarten at Hendy Road, a private school, near Mold. And when the family moved to Melai in the autumn of 1950 it was decided that John should continue there as a Monday to Friday boarder, before enrolling for his primary education at the Llanfair Talhaearn village school. Looking back now on those events of over fifty years ago makes for some kind of statement about social change and trust. Gordon would take the six year old on a Monday morning to meet the train at Denbigh Station to put him, together with his satchel and personal belongings, in the care of the guard for the journey to Mold. On arrival at the station, there was still a mile-long walk on his own to the school. Come Friday the child would retrace his steps back to the station, and thence to Denbigh, where he would be met by his father for the further ten mile journey back to Melai. That was probably a different caring society, before any talk of child abuse. With the Dr Beeching rail cuts of the early seventies, even the train link between Denbigh and Mold has gone! After the village school at Llanfair, John went on to Abergele Secondary Modern for a year, then on to Brookland Hall Boarding School for Boys, Welshpool. Here he showed great promise in woodcraft, and with competence succeeded in making furniture for the school chapel. Additionally becoming a Scout Leader there. When he left Brookland Hall as a sixteen year old, John took up a year's course at Llysfasi College of Agriculture Ruthin, and when he left to come home to the farm, continued for a further two years as a day-release student. This was a Farm Business Management course at which he passed with distinction.

We have noted elsewhere the excellent rapport that existed between John and his father when both worked together at Melai. The discussions and joint decisions resulting in a more streamlined operation: in 1968 the dairy cows were sold in favour of a suckler cow/beef/sheep system. This was a scheme which better suited the farm, giving the opportunity for mixed grazing on the top land and reducing competition for early spring grass on the meadows, to the benefit of the mothering ewes. The other important factor in this decision, was that the fact that the detergent used for cleansing the dairy utensils had an allergic effect on John's skin. So decision taken, a consignment of Blue Grey cows was purchased from Northumberland and the sheep numbers increased.

John was quite an enthusiastic sailor and was involved in the Tall Ships Race and keenly supported the fund raising efforts of the Abergele branch of the RNLI of which he was a one time chairman. And with his brother Roger sailed a dinghy at Rhos on Sea up to the time of his marriage. John married Margaret Reynolds, a young lady he had met through his involvement in the Colwyn Bay Sailing Club at Rhos on Sea, in 1968.

They had a family of two boys, both of whom were Harper

Adams educated. Daniel, now 28, is working for Peter Jones Livestock (PJL), a Tarporley based livestock marketing company, while James 26 works for BOCM as a farm management advisor.

Upon their marriage John and Margaret lived in Colomendy, the bungalow which was built on the site of the old pigeon house, but later swapped over with Mum and Dad Wilyman and moved into Melai farmhouse when the children came along.

At this time John was shouldering more responsibility. In 1978 a large sheep shed suitable for indoor lambing was erected with a capacity for 500 ewes. Lambing started in batches after Christmas, following a pre natal scanning regime, and the ewes and lambs let out three or four days after birth on to fresh pasture. As the ewes and lambs were let out, more pregnant sheep were brought in. As time went by John's interest in farm conservation grew. With advice from Trefor Thompson, the Forestry Officer for Clwyd County Council, a conservation expert, a selection of trees were planted, suitable nest boxes located and three ponds created. It was a system which was to attract a variety of wild water fowl, as well as indigenous and migratory birds. This was a source of avid family interest. It gained for them the coveted Lapwing Award made annually by Country Life magazine, and in 1988 the John Hooson Cup given to the top Conservationist of the Year in Clwyd. Under the stewardship of both John and Gordon Wilyman, Melai had become a beacon of enlightened farming, and both were happy to show and share their achievements. For example in May 1995 Melai was the venue of the National Sheep Association's 'Sheep 95 Wales' event which was attended by over 4000 farmers. While in October 1992 it was visited by Prime Minister John Major on a fact finding mission. Melai became a first choice for farm visits by Young Farmers Clubs, and other organizations with a rural interest including people from abroad.

But fate often does the strangest and most unexpected

things. Winnie became afflicted with Alzeimers Disease and died on the 21st of October, 1997, and John who had been first diagnosed with Motor Neurone Disease in August 1996, died seven months after his mother on June 21st, 1998. For the family this was the saddest time of all. Alzeimers had its more gradual effects but ultimately most devastating, depriving Winnie of her sharp mental faculties. This meant that she didn't know what was happening to John which in a sense was a blessing.

John, on the other hand, was in full possession of his thought processes almost to the end, even realising the inevitability of Motor Neurone's effects for which there was no known cure. It had originally affected him when he found difficulty with his hand movements and feeling, as he worked in the lambing shed. But it's effects in the last months of his life was a story of rapid degeneration. He could drive his car in the previous Christmas; by June John had passed away. He was 52 years of age.

For Gordon this was a devastating time, but stoic of character and resolve he carried on. He was now in his eighties, yet for another six years assisted by Daniel, John's eldest son, the farm work went on: Gordon now out of semi-retirement drew on his organizational skills, while Daniel provided hands-on expertise and youthful energy. 'We were a highly successful team,' Gordon says, paying handsome tribute to his running mate. Still Gordon would be seen supervising the sale of beef cattle at St Asaph auction. Up to the final decision to sell Melai in July 2002 he still did all the book keeping. As well as cooking and doing the domestic chores. That's the measure of this dynamic personality, Gordon Wilyman.

Now farming is behind him he can ease up, but that's only a relative term. He is a congenial man who enjoys the company of a wide circle of friends in a meal with a glass of wine. He is a member of the Clwyd Wine and Food Society who regularly meet at various venues to indulge their interests. He still makes time for holidays, and at the St Mary's Church at Llanfair

Talhaearn he regularly takes his turn reading the Lesson on Sunday.

To complete the Wilyman family album we have 53 year old Roger Wilyman, Gordon's other son who lives with his wife Gaynor, a community nurse based in Abergele, and their two sons, twenty one year old Richard (now in his 3rd year at Leeds doing business and marketing studies), and 14 year old George (in his 3rd year at Ysgol Emrys ap Iwan Abergele), at Pant y Clyd.

Pant y Clyd was once a cottage small holding on the Melai estate which had been sold off by Shadrach Davies.

Roger had purchased the buildings and farmstead back in the late seventies, then in a semi derelict state, with permission to restore the house; a work which he put in hand in 1980. Roger married Gaynor Davies, a farmer's daughter from Morfa Cwybr near Rhyl in 1982. Roger has always had a strong involvement in the farm: from his school days at Llanfair Talhaearn until he later left Abergele Grammar School at 18, this was his childhood leisure passion, which continued in his spare time until he married.

But clearly there was no place for the two boys at Melai, so urged by Gordon, Roger armed with a clutch of A level results, but not seeking college life, took up a trainee post at the Farnley Hall estate office, north of Otley in Yorkshire. Here on an estate in excess of 2,000 acres owned by the Horton Fawkes family, descendants of Guy Fawkes, Roger gained a useful 2 year experience in land management. On his return to Wales in 1970 he was taken on by the surveyors Peckover Burrill and Owen, and qualified as a Chartered Surveyor in 1973.

Some time afterwards he became a partner in the company, which later merged with Jones and Son to form the present practice of Jones Peckover.

As a rural practice Chartered Surveyor and Agricultural Valuer, Roger's work includes land and estate management; valuation; compulsory purchase compensation; pipeline easements, and landlord and tenant matters.

He is a valuer for the Agricultural Mortgage Corporation and an agricultural arbitrator.

As well as local landowners and farmers, his clients include 'The Representative Body of the Church in Wales', and the 'Crown Estate Commissioners' for their Wales and North West of England (fore-shore and marine interests).

Roger is an active member of the Royal Institution of Chartered Surveyors (RICS), a former branch chairman and, for 9 years, a member of the General Council which then became the International Governing Council.

Chapter 7

In Conversation – Reflections and Reminiscences.

Meurig Owen: You were born on March 2nd, 1915 while your father was away in the war in France, where he saw action in the fearful 'Battle of the Somme'. What are your childhood recollections?

Gordon Wilyman: My mother had a great deal to do, because my father wasn't there, so my relationship with my mother and my elder brother Ken who was around at the time, was a very happy one. We got on well together and we thought the world of her.

MO What was her name?

GW Margaret

MO You were at Wellesbourne in Warwickshire at that time. What sort of a place was it?

GW It was very much a country area. Wellesbourne then, was a very small village. An air station was set up there in the 1939 war, and it's now quite a big place with a large residential area, but it wasn't so when I was there.

MO What about school?

GW We went to the nearby farm of the Hobbs family where the butcher's daughter a Miss Hopkins, taught about seven of us in the farmhouse. Most were farmers sons and daughters from the neighbourhood. I remember very well that two of them came to 'school' every day on ponies.

MO What about the games you played? Were you athletic?

GW There were no athletics at that time, that came much later. It was a small village community and we played little games together, conkers when they were in season, but apart from that there was no organized sport or entertainment at all.

An interesting event comes to my mind thinking about childhood days. I remember my mother, before my father came home from the war, so I imagine that it must have been 1919; mother got my brother Ken and I up at seven o'clock one night. 'There's going to be a film,' she said. Now a film – we had never heard of, we didn't know what she was talking about. Just opposite our house there was a travelling show from the trenches showing what had gone on in France. And still images were projected on to a sheet, there was no plastic then, a linen screen just outside our house and we were absolutely amazed that we were seeing pictures of soldiers in France. That was the first time that I saw a 'film', not a movie, but an exciting experience for all that. And we got up to look at it through the bedroom window.

MO Later you moved from Wellesbourne . . .

GW Yes, to Handsworth near Birmingham. To start with I went to Grove Lane Council School there which in those days had about 100 children: to me coming from Miss Hopkins the butchers daughter, it was a huge establishment.

Following that I went to Aston Grammar, a King Edward Foundation School. I remember it well: it was very close to the HP sauce factory, and when they cleaned out the vats the area reeked with the smell of sauce. I've never had HP sauce since but my brother was not put off sauce at all, he was quite fond of it!

I then graduated to King Edward Grammar School which was less than half a mile from New Street Station, the main railway station in Birmingham.

At school my game was rugby, I played for the school team and again later when I went to Rease Heath. Perhaps surprisingly rugby was the game in the Midlands, even though the schools I went to were quite close to Aston Villa and West Bromwich Albion football grounds. But in school there wasn't any football at all.

MO Were the school years happy ones for you?

GW Yes . . . , but I wasn't scholastically minded. People say that school years are the happiest days of your life. My happiest was the day I left! I didn't dislike school, don't misunderstand me, yes I was happy at school, but I was so pleased when I left.

MO You had this yearning to be a farmer from an early age. Considering the prospects, hard work and little money, was there ever a time when you considered anything else? There were many other things you could have done . . .

GW It never entered my head to do anything else. Never crossed my mind, not once ever.

MO What was it about farming that gave you a buzz?

GW I suppose it was the country life and animals. I have always been fond of animals. And I think animals get on with me.

MO In your farming life have books featured strongly in acquiring farming knowledge, or was farming picked up working alongside skilled craftsmen and good farmers?

GW It was a combination of the two. Books certainly played a part. And the farming press. In the early years it was *The Farmer and Stockbreeder* – the *Farmers Weekly* came at a later stage.

MO What about books?

GW I read books by A.G. Street and people like that. They were excellent.

MO What about technical books?

GW At a later stage, yes. Perhaps it didn't sink in. After I went to Rease Heath and did the agricultural course there, books meant more to me. I was able to get more from technical books than I did before.

MO How much did you learn by your mistakes?

GW Yes, I certainly learnt from my mistakes. I couldn't specify any particular example at the moment. If you don't profit from your mistakes, then it's time to think of doing something else. And get out of it!

MO Your first go at farming on your own account was pig farming at Ewloe, a line of farming which had not featured to any large extent previously! Where had the interest come from? How did you learn about pigs?

GW I learnt about pigs while on the farms I worked on in Cheshire, before I went on my own. Two of these were big cheese making farms and pigs went with cheese making; the pigs consumed the whey which was a cheese by product. It was an excellent food for them with barley meal and so on. Yes, I had done a lot with pigs before. The farm at Huntington near Chester kept 100 milking cows and made cheese: they would always have 200 pigs on the farm. It doesn't sound much today where you have units of 2,000, but in those days it was a lot of pigs.

MO Pigs still featured in your farming when you first came to Melai. How large an enterprise was it, and what was the system?

GW Yes, breeding sows because there was plenty of rough grazing for them. And there were old buildings such as the disused laundry and old mill house which were not fit for anything else agriculturally. It was a matter of putting these old buildings to good use.

MO I remember that I sold you four young Essex Saddleback pigs at that time . . .

GW Yes, Saddlebacks were popular because they grazed well and were good mothers. They were crossed with a Large White boar, the Landrace came later.

   We converted looseboxes to accommodate a couple of hundred pigs.

MO You have said that you learnt about sheep farming from Bob Hughes, the shepherd at Melai. What about others who helped in the learning process: people like Nick Archdale, Meuric Rees and Edward Owen? Did anything of these people rub off on you?

GW Nick Archdale came out of the army and went to university. He hadn't a great deal of farming experience at that time so he had to learn rapidly.

   I was different because I'd been brought up from an early age with livestock. Meuric Rees, with sheep, was particularly knowledgeable.

MO And Edward Owen?

GW Well you see when I went with Edward Owen, it was
agreed that I did all the management. I would just talk
over the best policy of what the farm was going to be
engaged in, and it was up to me to put it into action.

I learnt quite a bit about shire horses and store cattle
from Edward Owen.

MO In 1979 you were awarded the OBE for your services to
agriculture: can you say something about that experience
at the Palace. And in June 1977 you were welcomed aboard
the Royal Yacht Britannia . . .

GW When I received the OBE I could nominate who would
come with me. My wife Winnie was one, naturally, and my
two sons. That was a great experience, to go to the Palace
then was really something. We went into one section of the
Palace for a briefing about the procedure and how we
should handle it. Which was good, because in those days
one rarely saw the Queen.

To go on the Royal Yacht was something I will never
forget because we were part of a party of only about 120
welcomed aboard. The Yacht was touring around Wales at
that time and was moored about a mile out from
Holyhead. We went from the quay at Holyhead, which
was totally secured, and invited aboard having shown our
tickets of authority, then, at about twelve to a boat we were
shuttled by tender to the Yacht. There we were briefly
presented to the Queen and the Duke, and from there
proceeded to the State Room. From then on it was a very
informal cocktail party with the Queen and the Duke
circulating around and talking to everyone, while the

officers on the Yacht acted as stewards seeing that everyone had enough to eat and drink. That was a real experience.

I suppose we were with the Royal Party in the Stateroom for a good hour and a half, then the Queen and the Duke got up and left for their private apartments: and the shuttle boats then picked us up to go back to Holyhead. It was a wonderful experience, no question about that. It was even better than going to the Palace: but that is probably down to my love of the sea.

MO I would like to ask about the Oxford Farming Conference: there you spoke about the 'Challenge of the Common Market'.

You were fairly optimistic. Was it a good thing for the British farmer?

GW Up to a point. Had we not gone into the Common Market we would be more in the cold. It brought in grants for agriculture which weren't available to us. Some of it was good, but it wasn't all good.

Whereas before entry into the EEC the government wanted greater production from the hills, grant aiding drainage and land reclamation, together with hard tracks to service them; now we are in almost total reversal. Farmers are quickly becoming merely park keepers. I am convinced now that the increased incidence of flooding is due to the policy of reclaiming the hill wetlands, those areas no longer retain the heavy rainfall on the hills as of yore.

MO Are we seeing changes in the country which mean the end of traditional ways?

GW I think, sadly, we are with increased reliance on vertical integration, and a growing emphasis on hill farmers in a park keeper role.

And there's a tendency towards bigger farm units.

MO What advice would you give to anyone wishing to come into the industry? What qualities are needed for successful farming?

GW Things have changed so much. With arable farming it's a different outlook and dairy herds are getting much bigger. It's sad to say, small herds are all going out. There are hardly any left.

We have seen the supermarkets doing their best to kill off livestock markets. They've been offering favourable prices for dead weight stock going direct to supermarkets in order to wind livestock markets down. And I've said for a long time, and many have agreed with me, if we don't keep the livestock markets open we will be totally in the hands of the supermarkets and they will nail farmers to the wall. I mean it's profits and share holders – that is all the supermarkets care about and that is a fact; it is happening and it's so sad.

A number of livestock markets still hold on, and that is because a number of us have supported them, otherwise they'd have gone out. I think it will be almost the death knell of the livestock industry if the supermarkets get complete control.

MO Coming back to the qualities of stockman ship and way of life. There will always be a place for a high standard of stockman ship . . .

GW Yes of course that will come into it, naturally. The fact now for British farmers is that everything has to be produced to the highest standards, including hygiene. I don't think that any farmer is against that, but there is a cost to what farmers are doing. The same standards are supposed to apply throughout Europe. Up to a point the British farmer plays the game according to the rules; there are some rare exceptions, of course there are. But in regard to France and regulations, I think they treat them as things to be circum-navigated rather than obeyed. And there are more clever people finding ways around the regulations than those making them. And so their cost of production, if they are not sticking to the rules are lower than they are over here. They add a lot to the cost.

I believe if everything was produced to the same standard throughout the EEC we would be competing on an even wicket. But they're not now unfortunately.

MO The Welsh Halfbred Sheep Breeders Association was a good example of what farmers can achieve by co-operating. Will co-operation among farmers ever come about in this country?

GW We don't co-operate. It's every man for himself in a way. In many parts of Europe they do co-operate in marketing their produce. But it is gradually coming here now. As I say it's every man for himself, and he does it to the best of his ability. But having said that, farmers are perfectly happy to pool their ideas and share their experiences.

MO Apart from membership of the NFU you are also a member of the Country Landowners Association. What benefits accrue from that?

GW The CLA is a good organisation and can provide useful help for farmers.

They've done a lot for the tenant/landlord system. And on legal matters they can give very good advice.

I joined in 1970 and for a time was on their Executive Committee, but I had to give it up because I could not give it enough time due to my National Farmers Union involvement.

MO What is your philosophy: I know that you are an early riser?

GW I'm not an early to bed either. I've always got up at six o'clock. I still do, its just the right time to get up.

MO Do you need a lot of sleep?

GW I think seven hours sleep is enough for anyone. After a fashion, the more sleep you have, the more you want. I do need more now that I'm getting older . . .

Chapter 8

Melai – A Place Steeped in History

Melai lies mid way between Llanfair Talhaearn, Llangernyw and Llansannan and was probably once a township in a hollow of surrounding hills: Moel Unben; Tyddyn Moel and the ffrithoedd, Hafod Talog and Ffrith Bedwyn.

It had its own water mill fed by a leat from Nant Melai (a tributary of the River Elwy), a laundry also using Nant Melai water, and a family Chapel near the house.

Up on the bank overlooking the farmstead stood the Colomendy, a two storey building, which was once used to breed pigeons for the kitchen table as well as conveying messages before the days of the Penny Post. This was a good roost to refresh their pigeon instincts, standing on an easily seen promontory !

There was also an enclosed rabbit warren, again to provide for the kitchen pot. While goats and native Welsh ponies inhabited the upper slopes. As for recreation there was a bowling green located on the site of the present sheep shed.

In asserting his belief that Ieuan ap Kenrich held the tenure of the land in 1334, the noted Welsh scholar Bob Owen Croesor confirms that 'Melai was a tithe township, and people like Madog ab Iorwerth, Einion ab Kenich, Dafydd ab Moreddig, Cadwaladr ab Gwilym, Adda ab Runon, Dafydd ab Cadwg and several others held portions or hereditaments of it'. Thus we can surmise that there was once a self supporting community centered on Melai with its facility for physical and spiritual regeneration.

But this valley settlement could have a history dating even earlier. For example, an estate survey of 1802 records the discovery of a 'tumulus containing jugs and vases'. These are referred to colloquially as *eirch potiau*, earthenware coffins, and were found in a field then called Dyffryn Uchaf now known as Caeau Dŵr.

Idwal Vaughan, whose family farmed at Melai up to 1945, says that such was the folklore about this field that it was never ploughed, out of respect to the departed, the belief being that this was an ancient cemetery. He says that the pots and their contents apparently disintegrated on being exposed to the elements. So clearly there were people living here in ancient times, possibly in the beaker period dating back to 1,500 years BC.

For centuries Melai was the home of the Wynn family which could claim descent from Marchudd ap Cynan Lord of Bryn Ffanigl, founder of the VIIIth Noble Tribe of North Wales and the 9th century chieftain who commanded the forces of Gwynedd under Rhodri Mawr (Roderick the Great) King of Wales. He was the ancestor of Ednyfed Fychan, the celebrated minister and general of Llywelyn the Great, a direct forebear of the royal house of Tudor.

Thus we find that the family tree though muddied by family intrigue can be traced down to Iorwerth y Penwyn – Edward the Whitehead progenitor of the Wynns of Melai and lived there about 1250-1290. It was a grandson of the said Iorwerth, Rhys ap Dafydd Llwyd who seemingly lived at Melai in the latter half of the 14th century.

In the family annals we find two eminent figures in Welsh literary and religious life: Edmund Prys, (1543-1623) Archdeacon of Meirioneth the eminent poet and scholar who is now best remembered for his metrical psalms, which were published as an appendix to the Welsh Book of Common Prayer, and up to the 18th century was virtually the only Hymnal used in Wales: and William Salesbury (1520-1584?) who was the first to translate the New Testament into Welsh.

The first member of the family to assume the surname of Wynne (or Wynn) was William Wynn ap Meredith. And it was a descendant of his, William Wynne, who married Mary a daughter of Sir Richard Clough and Catrin of Berain and thus brought with her a large dowry, the lands of the dissolved Abbey of Maenan.

Richard Clough is remembered today as a financial genius who, with Sir Thomas Gresham, represented Queen Elizabeth's interest at Antwerp the financial capital of the world at that time, and founded the Royal Exchange in London based on the Bourse at Antwerp. His wealth was legendary and it can be guessed that Mary, his co-heiress, brought with her untold affluence to Melai.

According to Bob Owen Croesor, the Wynns of Melai held positions of high esteem during the 16th to 18th centuries as High Sheriffs of Denbighshire. Many were famous scholars, some celebrated lawyers who held high office and figured prominently in the works of the family bards and harpists, who highly praised the hospitality given to them by the squires of Melai.

By marriages between the great families it can be shown how Melai fortunes prospered and strengthened. The Melai succession became part of the Glynllifon Estate when Jane Wynn a Melai heiress: daughter of John Wynn of Melai and Maenan, an MP, married Sir John Wynn, Bart., of Bodvean in 1736. It was their eldest son, Sir Thomas Wynn, who was elevated to the Irish peerage as the first Lord Newborough, who continued the Melai inheritance.

Thus Melai became a home farm of the Newborough family and was in their ownership until 1920 when it was acquired by William Vaughan. Large parcels of Newborough land and property in Denbighshire were sold in 1917 and again in 1920, land which stretched vastly from Llangernyw and Gwytherin up to the vicinity of Denbigh. It was in the latter tract of property sold, that Melai left the Newborough portfolio. So came to an end the thousand year unbroken ownership of Melai by the same family.

Melai was held by the Vaughan family up to 1945, then

farmed by Eluned (Vaughan) a Melai heiress who had married Arthur Moores a co-founder of Littlewoods, the well known Liverpool company. The next owner was Shadrach Davies, a farmer and cattle dealer, who held annual sales of store cattle there. Then it was sold again to Edward Owen in 1950 which is where we began the Gordon Wilyman story.

In a discussion on historical Melai there always arises the question of the name and its origins. Ask local people and they will declare stoutly in favour of Melai being a corruption of the Welsh *'mil'* which means 'a thousand'. As the home farm of a large estate Melai could have been part of a thousand acres and more. Certainly if the *'cynefin'* which was once part of the holding was included then, *'mil'*, a thousand acres would be possible.

The ancient name of Llannerch y Penwyn – Penwyn's Plain however is one which fits much easier, having regard to the hundred and twenty acre water meadow glade bordered by rising hills and the allusion to Iorwerth y Penwyn, famously the ancestor of the Wynn dynasty. Indeed that would be even more appropriate given the alternative translation of 'Penwyn' as 'Head of Wyn' rather than 'Whitehead', Iorwerth's supposed nickname. Because Llannerch y Penwyn would then translate as 'the glade or plain belonging to the head of the Wynn family'.

Melai with 'mil' as a derivative does not ring true and is hardly satisfactory. Professor Hywel Wyn Owen of the University of Wales Bangor, the leading authority on Welsh place names and their meaning, seems heavily inclined to Melai being a corruption of *'mêl'* the Welsh word for 'honey'. Continuing the analogy we get *'melys'* which means 'sweet'. So we then get the theory that here we have a place with sweet associations: a place with honey bees. Or a rivulet, Nant Melai, with its water, sweet to the taste, and perhaps having a mellowing effect on the water meadows.

Whatever the meaning, Melai is also a name of long

standing from a 'Meley' reference in 1334; in 1556-64 'Dyffryn Melei' (Vale of Melei) and again in 1700 further references to 'Mele'.

The honey associations could fit in well here too, indeed in Worcester we have Honeybourne, and in Kent, Honey Hill. It all has a nice feel to it. Nant Melai could translate nicely to Honey Brook, and in a warm valley such as this it could be entirely appropriate that this farm and township should be known as Melai.

Bibliography

Ellis Davies, *The Prehistoric and Roman Remains of Denbighshire.* Published 1929 – Printed by William Lewis Ltd, Cambrian Works, Cardiff.

W, Bezant Lowe, *The Heart of Northern Wales* (Volume 1 and 2). Published 1912 – Printed by W.E. Owen, Llanfairfechan.

J.Y.W. Lloyd, *The History of Powys Fadog* (Volume V). Published 1885 by Whiting & Co, London.

Eurwyn Wiliam, *Traditional Farm Buildings in North-East Wales 1550-1900.* Published 1982 by Welsh Folk Museum

R.O.F. Wynne, *The Wynne Family of Melai and Garthewin.* Reprinted from the Transactions, Volume 5 (1956) of the Denbighshire Historical Society.

The Twenty-Seventh Oxford Farming Conference at the Town Hall, Oxford January 8-10, 1973: *Report and Proceedings.*

Meurig Owen, *A Grand Tour of North Wales.* Published by Gwasg Carreg Gwalch, 2003.